What is Good Weather?

Whether the weather be cold,
Or whether the weather be hot,
We'll weather the weather
Whatever the weather
Whether we like it or not.

Traditional

Claire Llewellyn

OXFORD
UNIVERSITY PRESS

OXFORD
UNIVERSITY PRESS

Great Clarendon Street, Oxford OX2 6DP

Oxford University Press is a department of the University of Oxford.
It furthers the University's objective of excellence in research, scholarship,
and education by publishing worldwide in

Oxford New York

Athens Auckland Bangkok Bogotá Buenos Aires Calcutta
Cape Town Chennai Dar es Salaam Delhi Florence Hong Kong Istanbul
Karachi Kuala Lumpur Madrid Melbourne Mexico City Mumbai
Nairobi Paris São Paulo Singapore Taipei Tokyo Toronto Warsaw

with associated companies in Berlin Ibadan

Oxford is a registered trade mark of Oxford University Press
in the UK and in certain other countries

Published in the United Kingdom
by Oxford University Press

Text © Claire Llewellyn 2000

The moral rights of the author have been asserted

Database right Oxford University Press (maker)

First published 2000

British Library Cataloguing in Publication Data

Data available

ISBN 0 19 915705 7

Available in packs
Weather Pack of Six   (one of each book)   ISBN 0 19 915711 1
Weather Class Pack   (six of each book)   ISBN 0 19 915712 X

Printed in Hong Kong

Acknowledgements

The Publisher would like to thank the following for permission
to reproduce photographs:

John Cleare: p 21; Corbis/Yann Arthus-Bertrand: p 17 (top); Corel: front cover, title page, p 11 (top),
18, 22, 23 (bottom left), and back cover; Robert Harding Picture Library/Nigel Gomm: p 15 (left);
Robert Harding Picture Library/Mark Mawson: p 16; Robert Harding Picture Library /Kim Hart: p 19
(top); The Image Bank/ China Tourism Press/Wang, Miao: p 23 (top); Frank Lane Picture Agency/Ray
Bird: p 5 (bottom); Frank Lane Picture Agency/D. Cavagnaro/Sunset: p 6 (centre); Frank Lane Picture
Agency/D. Hall: p 6 (bottom); Frank Lane Picture Agency/A.A. Riley: p 9 (top); Frank Lane Picture
Agency/J. Hosking: p 9 (bottom); Frank Lane Picture Agency/H. D. Brandl: p 10; Frank Lane Picture
Agency/Roger Wilmshurst: p 11 (centre); Frank Lane Picture Agency/L. Batten: p 11 (bottom); Frank
Lane Picture Agency/D. Hall: p 15 (bottom); Frank Lane Picture Agency/Mark Newman: p 19 (centre);
Frank Lane Picture Agency/L.G. Nilsson/Skylight: p 20; Frank Lane Picture Agency/Mark Newman: p 23
(bottom right); National Geographic Society/Dick Durrance: p 8; National Geographic Society/Steve
Raymer: p 12; National Geographic Society/Melford Taylor: p 22 (top); National Aeronautics and Space
Administration: p 14; Press Association News/David Jones: p 17 (bottom); Royal National Lifeboat
Institution: p 13 (bottom); Science Photo Library/Alex Bertel: p 7 (centre); Science Photo Library/Shelia
Terry: p 7 (bottom); The Telegraph Colour Library/R. Sewell: p 5 (top); The Telegraph Colour Library/
B. Tanaka: p 13 (centre); The Telegraph Colour Library/Jean Guichard: p 22 (bottom right).

Illustrations by Chrome-Dome Design and Andy Cooke.

Contents

All kinds of weather

There are many different kinds of weather. It can be hot or cold, wet or dry, windy or still. Are some kinds of weather good weather? Are some kinds of weather bad?

People do not always agree about the weather. A farmer may be happy with a day of heavy rain, but somebody else may hate it.

The farmer of this crop will be pleased when it rains. ▶

These people are getting wet. They are not enjoying being in the rain. ◀

Hot and sunny

The sun can be good

When the sun shines brightly in a clear blue sky, it's fun to be outside. In summer you can swim, or ride your bike, or play in the street with your friends.

Warm, sunny weather helps plants to grow, and crops to ripen in the fields. A good **harvest** provides plenty of food for people and animals.

We can use the sun's energy to make **electricity** to heat and light our homes. **Solar energy** is clean and it will never run out. It can always be used even when the weather is cloudy.

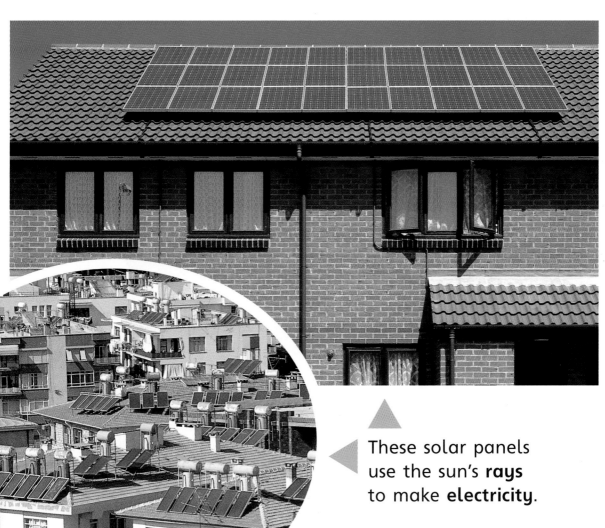

These solar panels use the sun's **rays** to make **electricity**.

The sun can be bad

We need to protect ourselves from the sun. Its strong **rays** can burn our skin. This can harm our bodies and make us very ill.

When a forest fire starts, it may take many firefighters to put it out.

Hot, sunny weather makes things dry out. Plants get so dry that they catch fire easily. Forest fires can burn for days, destroying hundreds of trees and animals.

Long spells of dry weather are called **droughts**. A drought can make ponds and rivers dry up. Animals cannot live without fresh water, so many of them die in droughts.

A river before a **drought**.

A river during a drought.

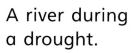

Wind

Windy weather can be good

It is fun to fly a kite on a windy day. The wind tugs the kite and lifts it high into the sky. Sometimes the wind can be so strong that it pulls you along with the kite.

The wind helps plants to spread. It blows their seeds to new places where there is room to grow.

For thousands of years, people have used the wind to power their ships across the water.

Windmills once used the wind to grind grain.

Now windmills are used to make **electricity**. Wind power is clean and will never run out.

Windy weather can be bad

Sometimes the wind is very strong. It blows very fast and it can be very noisy. Strong winds can damage buildings and cars, trees and crops.

The biggest wind storms are called **hurricanes**. They roar in from the sea and can blow up to 160 km per hour. Most hurricanes happen in hot countries.

Hurricane winds can destroy whole towns.

Strong winds at sea are very dangerous. The winds whip up high waves which can sink ships. Many sailors have died because their ships sank in storms.

This ship was sunk by a **typhoon** near Pohnpei Island, Micronesia.

Lifeboats rescue sailors during storms at sea.

Rain

Rain can be good

Rain often makes the air feel clean and fresh. You can have great fun splashing in all the puddles.

Rain is important for animals, people and plants. Without rain, the world would be dry with no rivers or seas. Nothing can grow or live without rain.

The moon is ▶ a dry, dusty place. Without rain, the earth might look like this.

In some of the hottest parts of the world, rain only falls for a few weeks in the year. It fills the rivers and waters the crops. It is so welcome that people dance and play in the streets.

These children are happy that the rain has come.

This desert in Mexico is filled with flowers after rain.

Rain can be bad

Wet weather can make people gloomy when it spoils their plans. You cannot have a picnic in heavy rain or a day out by the sea. Rain spoils sports matches and parties.

 This tennis match had to stop because of the rain.

Too much rain can
cause great damage.
Rivers get so full
that water rises
above the banks and
floods over the land.
Floods ruin people's
homes. Very bad
floods sweep away
people and animals
and drown them.

These people are being
rescued during a flood in
Shrewsbury, UK.

Snow

Snow can be good

It is great to be outside on a snowy day. You can build snowmen, throw snowballs at your friends or go sledging.

Ski resorts are full of **tourists** in the winter.

Many people love to snowboard or ski in the snow. Every year, millions of **tourists** go on holiday in the mountains. Many people get jobs in hotels and shops where tourists visit.

Snow can actually keep you warm. The air inside this snow shelter will soon warm up. It will be warmer than the air outside.

Snow is made of frozen water. In spring, the snow melts and flows into rivers. Like rain, it provides water for animals, plants and people.

Snowy days can be bad

Snow makes it difficult to get around. It is so slippery that you can fall over and hurt yourself.

Snow causes problems on the roads. Cars get stuck in **snowdrifts**, or crash into one another. At airports and stations, the planes and trains stop running or they are many hours late.

Heavy snow can bury farm animals.
Snow can be deadly on mountains.
When the snow builds up and gets too
heavy it crashes down the side of a
mountain. This is called an **avalanche**.
Avalanches sometimes bury buildings
and people.

What is good weather?

The weather is important to everyone. It gives us the water we need to survive. It helps plants to grow and provide us with food.

What kind of weather is bad weather? Hurricanes, floods and snow can kill people, and damage buildings. Most people would agree that they are all bad weather.

But what about the weather we have most of the time – the days of sun, rain, wind and snow?

Which pictures do you think show good weather? Which ones do you think show bad weather?

Glossary

avalanche A large pile of snow that crashes down the side of a mountain.

drought A long spell of dry weather.

electricity A kind of energy that can be used to make machines work.

harvest The farm crops that are picked from the fields.

hurricane A wind storm that begins over the sea near hot countries. It brings heavy rain and dangerous winds.

ray Beam of sunlight.

snowdrift A deep pile of snow that has been blown by the wind.

solar energy Power from the sun.

tourist A person who travels for interest or fun.

typhoon a form of hurricane that happens around India.

Index